Hockey Journal
Personal stats & Notebook

D1268669

Index

Game

26	
27	
28	
29	
30	
31	
32	
33	
34	
35	
36	
37	
38	
39	
40	
41	
42	
43	
44	
45	
46	
47	
48	
49	
50	

Game

51	
52	
53	
54	
55	
56	
57	
58	
59	
60	
61	
62	
63	
64	
65	
66	
67	
68	
69	
70	
71	
72	
73	
74	
75	

Game

76	
77	
78	
79	
80	
81	
82	
83	
84	
85	
86	
87	
88	
89	
90	
91	
92	
93	
94	
95	
96	
97	
98	
99	
100	

Game

101	
102	
103	
104	
105	
106	
107	
108	
109	
110	
111	
112	
113	
114	
115	
116	
117	
118	
119	
120	
121	
122	
123	
124	
125	

FINAL SCORE			VISITOR
			HOME

Date : _____ Hockey league level : _____

City : _____

Arena : _____

My Team : _____

Opponent : _____

Position : _____ Jersey Number : _____

Goals : _____ Assists : _____ Points : _____ Shots taken : _____

Power play goals : _____ Short handed goals : _____

Overtime goal : _____ Shoot out goal : _____ Game winning goal : ☐

Penalties : _____ Penality minutes : _____ +/- : _____ Hits : _____

Favorite game memory : _____
_____

Game Notes : _____
_____
_____
_____
_____
_____
_____
_____

FINAL SCORE			VISITOR
			HOME

Date : _____ Hockey league level : _____

City : _____

Arena : _____

My Team : _____

Opponent : _____

Position : _____ Jersey Number : _____

Goals : _____ Assists : _____ Points : _____ Shots taken : _____

Power play goals : _____ Short handed goals : _____

Overtime goal : _____ Shoot out goal : _____ Game winning goal : ☐

Penalties : _____ Penality minutes : _____ +/- : _____ Hits : _____

Favorite game memory : _____

_____

Game Notes : _____

_____

_____

_____

_____

_____

_____

_____

FINAL SCORE			VISITOR
			HOME

Date : _____ Hockey league level : _____

City : _____

Arena : _____

My Team : _____

Opponent : _____

Position : _____ Jersey Number : _____

Goals : _____ Assists : _____ Points : _____ Shots taken : _____

Power play goals : _____ Short handed goals : _____

Overtime goal : _____ Shoot out goal : _____ Game winning goal : ☐

Penalties : _____ Penality minutes : _____ +/- : _____ Hits : _____

Favorite game memory : _____
_____

Game Notes : _____
_____
_____
_____
_____
_____
_____
_____

3

FINAL SCORE			VISITOR
			HOME

Date : _____ Hockey league level : _____

City : _____

Arena : _____

My Team : _____

Opponent : _____

Position : _____ Jersey Number : _____

Goals : _____ Assists : _____ Points : _____ Shots taken : _____

Power play goals : _____ Short handed goals : _____

Overtime goal : _____ Shoot out goal : _____ Game winning goal : ☐

Penalties : _____ Penality minutes : _____ +/- : _____ Hits : _____

Favorite game memory : _____

_____

Game Notes : _____

_____

_____

_____

_____

_____

_____

_____

FINAL SCORE			VISITOR
			HOME

Date : _____ Hockey league level : _____

City : _____

Arena : _____

My Team : _____

Opponent : _____

Position : _____ Jersey Number : _____

Goals : _____ Assists : _____ Points : _____ Shots taken : _____

Power play goals : _____ Short handed goals : _____

Overtime goal : _____ Shoot out goal : _____ Game winning goal : ☐

Penalties : _____ Penality minutes : _____ +/- : _____ Hits : _____

Favorite game memory : _____

Game Notes : _____

FINAL SCORE			VISITOR
			HOME

Date : _____ Hockey league level : _____

City : _____

Arena : _____

My Team : _____

Opponent : _____

Position : _____ Jersey Number : _____

Goals : _____ Assists : _____ Points : _____ Shots taken : _____

Power play goals : _____ Short handed goals : _____

Overtime goal : _____ Shoot out goal : _____ Game winning goal : ☐

Penalties : _____ Penality minutes : _____ +/- : _____ Hits : _____

Favorite game memory : _____

Game Notes : _____
_____
_____
_____
_____
_____
_____
_____

FINAL SCORE			VISITOR
			HOME

Date : _____ Hockey league level : _____

City : _____

Arena : _____

My Team : _____

Opponent : _____

Position : _____ Jersey Number : _____

Goals : _____ Assists : _____ Points : _____ Shots taken : _____

Power play goals : _____ Short handed goals : _____

Overtime goal : _____ Shoot out goal : _____ Game winning goal : ☐

Penalties : _____ Penality minutes : _____ +/- : _____ Hits : _____

Favorite game memory : _____

_____

Game Notes : _____

_____

_____

_____

_____

_____

_____

_____

<table>
<tr><td rowspan="2">FINAL
SCORE</td><td></td><td></td><td>VISITOR</td></tr>
<tr><td></td><td></td><td>HOME</td></tr>
</table>

Date : _____ **Hockey league level :** _____

City : _____

Arena : _____

My Team : _____

Opponent : _____

Position : _____ **Jersey Number :** _____

Goals : _____ **Assists :** _____ **Points :** _____ **Shots taken :** _____

Power play goals : _____ **Short handed goals :** _____

Overtime goal : _____ **Shoot out goal :** _____ **Game winning goal :** ☐

Penalties : _____ **Penality minutes :** _____ **+/- :** _____ **Hits :** _____

Favorite game memory : _____
_____

Game Notes : _____
_____
_____
_____
_____
_____
_____
_____

FINAL SCORE			VISITOR
			HOME

Date : _____ Hockey league level : _____

City : _____

Arena : _____

My Team : _____

Opponent : _____

Position : _____ Jersey Number : _____

Goals : _____ Assists : _____ Points : _____ Shots taken : _____

Power play goals : _____ Short handed goals : _____

Overtime goal : _____ Shoot out goal : _____ Game winning goal : ☐

Penalties : _____ Penality minutes : _____ +/- : _____ Hits : _____

Favorite game memory : _____
_____

Game Notes : _____
_____
_____
_____
_____
_____
_____
_____

FINAL SCORE			VISITOR
			HOME

Date : _____ Hockey league level : _____

City : _____

Arena : _____

My Team : _____

Opponent : _____

Position : _____ Jersey Number : _____

Goals : _____ Assists : _____ Points : _____ Shots taken : _____

Power play goals : _____ Short handed goals : _____

Overtime goal : _____ Shoot out goal : _____ Game winning goal : ☐

Penalties : _____ Penality minutes : _____ +/- : _____ Hits : _____

Favorite game memory : _____
_____

Game Notes : _____
_____
_____
_____
_____
_____
_____
_____

FINAL SCORE			VISITOR
			HOME

Date : _____ Hockey league level : _____

City : _____

Arena : _____

My Team : _____

Opponent : _____

Position : _____ Jersey Number : _____

Goals : _____ Assists : _____ Points : _____ Shots taken : _____

Power play goals : _____ Short handed goals : _____

Overtime goal : _____ Shoot out goal : _____ Game winning goal : ☐

Penalties : _____ Penality minutes : _____ +/- : _____ Hits : _____

Favorite game memory : _____
_____

Game Notes : _____
_____
_____
_____
_____
_____
_____
_____

FINAL SCORE				VISITOR
				HOME

Date : _____ Hockey league level : _____

City : _____

Arena : _____

My Team : _____

Opponent : _____

Position : _____ Jersey Number : _____

Goals : _____ Assists : _____ Points : _____ Shots taken : _____

Power play goals : _____ Short handed goals : _____

Overtime goal : _____ Shoot out goal : _____ Game winning goal : ☐

Penalties : _____ Penality minutes : _____ +/- : _____ Hits : _____

Favorite game memory : _____
_____

Game Notes : _____
_____
_____
_____
_____
_____
_____
_____

FINAL SCORE			VISITOR
			HOME

Date : _____ Hockey league level : _____

City : _____

Arena : _____

My Team : _____

Opponent : _____

Position : _____ Jersey Number : _____

Goals : _____ Assists : _____ Points : _____ Shots taken : _____

Power play goals : _____ Short handed goals : _____

Overtime goal : _____ Shoot out goal : _____ Game winning goal : ☐

Penalties : _____ Penality minutes : _____ +/- : _____ Hits : _____

Favorite game memory : _____
_____

Game Notes : _____
_____
_____
_____
_____
_____
_____
_____

FINAL SCORE			VISITOR
			HOME

Date : _____ Hockey league level : _____

City : _____

Arena : _____

My Team : _____

Opponent : _____

Position : _____ Jersey Number : _____

Goals : _____ Assists : _____ Points : _____ Shots taken : _____

Power play goals : _____ Short handed goals : _____

Overtime goal : _____ Shoot out goal : _____ Game winning goal : ☐

Penalties : _____ Penality minutes : _____ +/- : _____ Hits : _____

Favorite game memory : _____
_____

Game Notes : _____
_____
_____
_____
_____
_____
_____
_____
_____

FINAL SCORE			VISITOR
			HOME

Date : _____ Hockey league level : _____

City : _____

Arena : _____

My Team : _____

Opponent : _____

Position : _____ Jersey Number : _____

Goals : _____ Assists : _____ Points : _____ Shots taken : _____

Power play goals : _____ Short handed goals : _____

Overtime goal : _____ Shoot out goal : _____ Game winning goal : ☐

Penalties : _____ Penality minutes : _____ +/- : _____ Hits : _____

Favorite game memory : _____

Game Notes : _____

FINAL SCORE			VISITOR
			HOME

Date : _____ Hockey league level : _____

City : _____

Arena : _____

My Team : _____

Opponent : _____

Position : _____ Jersey Number : _____

Goals : _____ Assists : _____ Points : _____ Shots taken : _____

Power play goals : _____ Short handed goals : _____

Overtime goal : _____ Shoot out goal : _____ Game winning goal : ☐

Penalties : _____ Penality minutes : _____ +/- : _____ Hits : _____

Favorite game memory : _____

_____

Game Notes : _____

_____

_____

_____

_____

_____

_____

_____

FINAL SCORE			VISITOR
			HOME

Date : _____ Hockey league level : _____

City : _____

Arena : _____

My Team : _____

Opponent : _____

Position : _____ Jersey Number : _____

Goals : _____ Assists : _____ Points : _____ Shots taken : _____

Power play goals : _____ Short handed goals : _____

Overtime goal : _____ Shoot out goal : _____ Game winning goal : ☐

Penalties : _____ Penality minutes : _____ +/- : _____ Hits : _____

Favorite game memory : _____

_____

Game Notes : _____

_____

_____

_____

_____

_____

_____

_____

FINAL SCORE			VISITOR
			HOME

Date : _____ Hockey league level : _____

City : _____

Arena : _____

My Team : _____

Opponent : _____

Position : _____ Jersey Number : _____

Goals : _____ Assists : _____ Points : _____ Shots taken : _____

Power play goals : _____ Short handed goals : _____

Overtime goal : _____ Shoot out goal : _____ Game winning goal : ☐

Penalties : _____ Penality minutes : _____ +/- : _____ Hits : _____

Favorite game memory : _____

_____

Game Notes : _____

_____

_____

_____

_____

_____

_____

_____

FINAL SCORE			VISITOR
			HOME

Date : _____ Hockey league level : _____

City : _____

Arena : _____

My Team : _____

Opponent : _____

Position : _____ Jersey Number : _____

Goals : _____ Assists : _____ Points : _____ Shots taken : _____

Power play goals : _____ Short handed goals : _____

Overtime goal : _____ Shoot out goal : _____ Game winning goal : ☐

Penalties : _____ Penality minutes : _____ +/- : _____ Hits : _____

Favorite game memory : _____

_____

Game Notes : _____

_____

_____

_____

_____

_____

_____

_____

FINAL SCORE			VISITOR
			HOME

Date : _____ Hockey league level : _____

City : _____

Arena : _____

My Team : _____

Opponent : _____

Position : _____ Jersey Number : _____

Goals : _____ Assists : _____ Points : _____ Shots taken : _____

Power play goals : _____ Short handed goals : _____

Overtime goal : _____ Shoot out goal : _____ Game winning goal : ☐

Penalties : _____ Penality minutes : _____ +/- : _____ Hits : _____

Favorite game memory : _____

_____

Game Notes : _____

_____

_____

_____

_____

_____

_____

_____

FINAL SCORE			VISITOR
			HOME

Date : _____ **Hockey league level :** _____

City : _____

Arena : _____

My Team : _____

Opponent : _____

Position : _____ **Jersey Number :** _____

Goals : _____ **Assists :** _____ **Points :** _____ **Shots taken :** _____

Power play goals : _____ **Short handed goals :** _____

Overtime goal : _____ **Shoot out goal :** _____ **Game winning goal :** ☐

Penalties : _____ **Penality minutes :** _____ **+/- :** _____ **Hits :** _____

Favorite game memory : _____

_____

Game Notes : _____

_____

_____

_____

_____

_____

_____

_____

FINAL SCORE			VISITOR
			HOME

Date : _____ Hockey league level : _____

City : _____

Arena : _____

My Team : _____

Opponent : _____

Position : _____ Jersey Number : _____

Goals : _____ Assists : _____ Points : _____ Shots taken : _____

Power play goals : _____ Short handed goals : _____

Overtime goal : _____ Shoot out goal : _____ Game winning goal : ☐

Penalties : _____ Penality minutes : _____ +/- : _____ Hits : _____

Favorite game memory : _____

_____

Game Notes : _____

_____

_____

_____

_____

_____

_____

_____

_____

FINAL SCORE			VISITOR
			HOME

Date : _____   Hockey league level : _____

City : _____

Arena : _____

My Team : _____

Opponent : _____

Position : _____   Jersey Number : _____

Goals : _____   Assists : _____   Points : _____   Shots taken : _____

Power play goals : _____   Short handed goals : _____

Overtime goal : _____   Shoot out goal : _____   Game winning goal : ☐

Penalties : _____   Penality minutes : _____   +/- : _____   Hits : _____

Favorite game memory : _____
_____

Game Notes : _____
_____
_____
_____
_____
_____
_____

FINAL SCORE			VISITOR
			HOME

Date : _____ Hockey league level : _____

City : _____

Arena : _____

My Team : _____

Opponent : _____

Position : _____ Jersey Number : _____

Goals : _____ Assists : _____ Points : _____ Shots taken : _____

Power play goals : _____ Short handed goals : _____

Overtime goal : _____ Shoot out goal : _____ Game winning goal : ☐

Penalties : _____ Penality minutes : _____ +/- : _____ Hits : _____

Favorite game memory : _____

_____

Game Notes : _____

_____

_____

_____

_____

_____

_____

_____

FINAL SCORE			VISITOR
			HOME

Date : _____ Hockey league level : _____

City : _____

Arena : _____

My Team : _____

Opponent : _____

Position : _____ Jersey Number : _____

Goals : _____ Assists : _____ Points : _____ Shots taken : _____

Power play goals : _____ Short handed goals : _____

Overtime goal : _____ Shoot out goal : _____ Game winning goal : ☐

Penalties : _____ Penality minutes : _____ +/- : _____ Hits : _____

Favorite game memory : _____
_____

Game Notes : _____
_____
_____
_____
_____
_____
_____
_____
_____

FINAL SCORE			VISITOR
			HOME

Date : _____ Hockey league level : _____

City : _____

Arena : _____

My Team : _____

Opponent : _____

Position : _____ Jersey Number : _____

Goals : _____ Assists : _____ Points : _____ Shots taken : _____

Power play goals : _____ Short handed goals : _____

Overtime goal : _____ Shoot out goal : _____ Game winning goal : ☐

Penalties : _____ Penality minutes : _____ +/- : _____ Hits : _____

Favorite game memory : _____

_____

Game Notes : _____

_____

_____

_____

_____

_____

_____

_____

FINAL SCORE			VISITOR
			HOME

Date : _____   Hockey league level : _____

City : _____

Arena : _____

My Team : _____

Opponent : _____

Position : _____   Jersey Number : _____

Goals : _____ Assists : _____ Points : _____ Shots taken : _____

Power play goals : _____   Short handed goals : _____

Overtime goal : _____ Shoot out goal : _____ Game winning goal : ☐

Penalties : _____ Penality minutes : _____ +/- : _____ Hits : _____

Favorite game memory : _____
_____

Game Notes : _____
_____
_____
_____
_____
_____
_____
_____

FINAL SCORE			VISITOR
			HOME

Date : _____ Hockey league level : _____

City : _____

Arena : _____

My Team : _____

Opponent : _____

Position : _____ Jersey Number : _____

Goals : _____ Assists : _____ Points : _____ Shots taken : _____

Power play goals : _____ Short handed goals : _____

Overtime goal : _____ Shoot out goal : _____ Game winning goal : ☐

Penalties : _____ Penality minutes : _____ +/- : _____ Hits : _____

Favorite game memory : _____
_____

Game Notes : _____
_____
_____
_____
_____
_____
_____
_____
_____

FINAL SCORE			VISITOR
			HOME

Date : _____   Hockey league level : _____

City : _____

Arena : _____

My Team : _____

Opponent : _____

Position : _____   Jersey Number : _____

Goals : _____   Assists : _____   Points : _____   Shots taken : _____

Power play goals : _____   Short handed goals : _____

Overtime goal : _____   Shoot out goal : _____   Game winning goal : ☐

Penalties : _____   Penality minutes : _____   +/- : _____   Hits : _____

Favorite game memory : _____
_____

Game Notes : _____
_____
_____
_____
_____
_____
_____
_____

FINAL SCORE			VISITOR
			HOME

Date : _____ Hockey league level : _____

City : _____

Arena : _____

My Team : _____

Opponent : _____

Position : _____ Jersey Number : _____

Goals : _____ Assists : _____ Points : _____ Shots taken : _____

Power play goals : _____ Short handed goals : _____

Overtime goal : _____ Shoot out goal : _____ Game winning goal : ☐

Penalties : _____ Penality minutes : _____ +/- : _____ Hits : _____

Favorite game memory : _____

_____

Game Notes : _____

_____

_____

_____

_____

_____

_____

_____

FINAL SCORE			VISITOR
			HOME

Date : _____ Hockey league level : _____

City : _____

Arena : _____

My Team : _____

Opponent : _____

Position : _____ Jersey Number : _____

Goals : _____ Assists : _____ Points : _____ Shots taken : _____

Power play goals : _____ Short handed goals : _____

Overtime goal : _____ Shoot out goal : _____ Game winning goal : ☐

Penalties : _____ Penality minutes : _____ +/- : _____ Hits : _____

Favorite game memory : _____
_____

Game Notes : _____
_____
_____
_____
_____
_____
_____

FINAL SCORE			VISITOR
			HOME

Date : _____ Hockey league level : _____

City : _____

Arena : _____

My Team : _____

Opponent : _____

Position : _____ Jersey Number : _____

Goals : _____ Assists : _____ Points : _____ Shots taken : _____

Power play goals : _____ Short handed goals : _____

Overtime goal : _____ Shoot out goal : _____ Game winning goal : ☐

Penalties : _____ Penality minutes : _____ +/- : _____ Hits : _____

Favorite game memory : _____

_____

Game Notes : _____

_____

_____

_____

_____

_____

_____

_____

FINAL SCORE			VISITOR
			HOME

Date : _____ Hockey league level : _____

City : _____

Arena : _____

My Team : _____

Opponent : _____

Position : _____ Jersey Number : _____

Goals : _____ Assists : _____ Points : _____ Shots taken : _____

Power play goals : _____ Short handed goals : _____

Overtime goal : _____ Shoot out goal : _____ Game winning goal : ☐

Penalties : _____ Penality minutes : _____ +/- : _____ Hits : _____

Favorite game memory : _____
_____

Game Notes : _____
_____
_____
_____
_____
_____
_____
_____

FINAL SCORE			VISITOR
			HOME

Date : _____ Hockey league level : _____

City : _____

Arena : _____

My Team : _____

Opponent : _____

Position : _____ Jersey Number : _____

Goals : _____ Assists : _____ Points : _____ Shots taken : _____

Power play goals : _____ Short handed goals : _____

Overtime goal : _____ Shoot out goal : _____ Game winning goal : ☐

Penalties : _____ Penality minutes : _____ +/- : _____ Hits : _____

Favorite game memory : _____
_____

Game Notes : _____
_____
_____
_____
_____
_____
_____
_____

FINAL SCORE			VISITOR
			HOME

Date : _____ Hockey league level : _____

City : _____

Arena : _____

My Team : _____

Opponent : _____

Position : _____ Jersey Number : _____

Goals : _____ Assists : _____ Points : _____ Shots taken : _____

Power play goals : _____ Short handed goals : _____

Overtime goal : _____ Shoot out goal : _____ Game winning goal : ☐

Penalties : _____ Penality minutes : _____ +/- : _____ Hits : _____

Favorite game memory : _____

Game Notes : _____

FINAL SCORE			VISITOR
			HOME

Date : _____ Hockey league level : _____

City : _____

Arena : _____

My Team : _____

Opponent : _____

Position : _____ Jersey Number : _____

Goals : _____ Assists : _____ Points : _____ Shots taken : _____

Power play goals : _____ Short handed goals : _____

Overtime goal : _____ Shoot out goal : _____ Game winning goal : ☐

Penalties : _____ Penality minutes : _____ +/- : _____ Hits : _____

Favorite game memory : _____
_____

Game Notes : _____
_____
_____
_____
_____
_____
_____
_____

FINAL SCORE			VISITOR
			HOME

Date : _____ Hockey league level : _____

City : _____

Arena : _____

My Team : _____

Opponent : _____

Position : _____ Jersey Number : _____

Goals : _____ Assists : _____ Points : _____ Shots taken : _____

Power play goals : _____ Short handed goals : _____

Overtime goal : _____ Shoot out goal : _____ Game winning goal : ☐

Penalties : _____ Penality minutes : _____ +/- : _____ Hits : _____

Favorite game memory : _____
_____

Game Notes : _____
_____
_____
_____
_____
_____
_____
_____

FINAL SCORE			VISITOR
			HOME

Date : _____ **Hockey league level :** _____

City : _____

Arena : _____

My Team : _____

Opponent : _____

Position : _____ **Jersey Number :** _____

Goals : _____ **Assists :** _____ **Points :** _____ **Shots taken :** _____

Power play goals : _____ **Short handed goals :** _____

Overtime goal : _____ **Shoot out goal :** _____ **Game winning goal :** ☐

Penalties : _____ **Penality minutes :** _____ **+/- :** _____ **Hits :** _____

Favorite game memory : _____
_____

Game Notes : _____
_____
_____
_____
_____
_____
_____
_____

FINAL SCORE			VISITOR
			HOME

Date : _____ Hockey league level : _____

City : _____

Arena : _____

My Team : _____

Opponent : _____

Position : _____ Jersey Number : _____

Goals : _____ Assists : _____ Points : _____ Shots taken : _____

Power play goals : _____ Short handed goals : _____

Overtime goal : _____ Shoot out goal : _____ Game winning goal : ☐

Penalties : _____ Penality minutes : _____ +/- : _____ Hits : _____

Favorite game memory : _____

_____

Game Notes : _____

_____

_____

_____

_____

_____

_____

_____

FINAL SCORE			VISITOR
			HOME

Date : _____ Hockey league level : _____

City : _____

Arena : _____

My Team : _____

Opponent : _____

Position : _____ Jersey Number : _____

Goals : _____ Assists : _____ Points : _____ Shots taken : _____

Power play goals : _____ Short handed goals : _____

Overtime goal : _____ Shoot out goal : _____ Game winning goal : ☐

Penalties : _____ Penality minutes : _____ +/- : _____ Hits : _____

Favorite game memory : _____

Game Notes : _____
_____
_____
_____
_____
_____
_____
_____

FINAL SCORE			VISITOR
			HOME

Date : _____ Hockey league level : _____

City : _____

Arena : _____

My Team : _____

Opponent : _____

Position : _____ Jersey Number : _____

Goals : _____ Assists : _____ Points : _____ Shots taken : _____

Power play goals : _____ Short handed goals : _____

Overtime goal : _____ Shoot out goal : _____ Game winning goal : ☐

Penalties : _____ Penality minutes : _____ +/- : _____ Hits : _____

Favorite game memory : _____
_____

Game Notes : _____
_____
_____
_____
_____
_____
_____
_____

FINAL SCORE			VISITOR
			HOME

Date : _____ Hockey league level : _____

City : _____

Arena : _____

My Team : _____

Opponent : _____

Position : _____ Jersey Number : _____

Goals : _____ Assists : _____ Points : _____ Shots taken : _____

Power play goals : _____ Short handed goals : _____

Overtime goal : _____ Shoot out goal : _____ Game winning goal : ☐

Penalties : _____ Penality minutes : _____ +/- : _____ Hits : _____

Favorite game memory : _____
_____

Game Notes : _____
_____
_____
_____
_____
_____
_____
_____

FINAL SCORE			VISITOR
			HOME

Date : _____ Hockey league level : _____

City : _____

Arena : _____

My Team : _____

Opponent : _____

Position : _____ Jersey Number : _____

Goals : _____ Assists : _____ Points : _____ Shots taken : _____

Power play goals : _____ Short handed goals : _____

Overtime goal : _____ Shoot out goal : _____ Game winning goal : ☐

Penalties : _____ Penality minutes : _____ +/- : _____ Hits : _____

Favorite game memory : _____
_____

Game Notes : _____
_____
_____
_____
_____
_____
_____
_____

FINAL SCORE			VISITOR
			HOME

Date : _____ Hockey league level : _____

City : _____

Arena : _____

My Team : _____

Opponent : _____

Position : _____ Jersey Number : _____

Goals : _____ Assists : _____ Points : _____ Shots taken : _____

Power play goals : _____ Short handed goals : _____

Overtime goal : _____ Shoot out goal : _____ Game winning goal : ☐

Penalties : _____ Penality minutes : _____ +/- : _____ Hits : _____

Favorite game memory : _____

_____

Game Notes : _____

_____

_____

_____

_____

_____

_____

_____

FINAL SCORE			VISITOR
			HOME

Date : _____ Hockey league level : _____

City : _____

Arena : _____

My Team : _____

Opponent : _____

Position : _____ Jersey Number : _____

Goals : _____ Assists : _____ Points : _____ Shots taken : _____

Power play goals : _____ Short handed goals : _____

Overtime goal : _____ Shoot out goal : _____ Game winning goal : ☐

Penalties : _____ Penality minutes : _____ +/- : _____ Hits : _____

Favorite game memory : _____

_____

Game Notes : _____

_____

_____

_____

_____

_____

_____

_____

FINAL SCORE			VISITOR
			HOME

Date : _____ Hockey league level : _____

City : _____

Arena : _____

My Team : _____

Opponent : _____

Position : _____ Jersey Number : _____

Goals : _____ Assists : _____ Points : _____ Shots taken : _____

Power play goals : _____ Short handed goals : _____

Overtime goal : _____ Shoot out goal : _____ Game winning goal : ☐

Penalties : _____ Penality minutes : _____ +/- : _____ Hits : _____

Favorite game memory : _____
_____

Game Notes : _____
_____
_____
_____
_____
_____
_____
_____

FINAL SCORE			VISITOR
			HOME

Date : _____ Hockey league level : _____

City : _____

Arena : _____

My Team : _____

Opponent : _____

Position : _____ Jersey Number : _____

Goals : _____ Assists : _____ Points : _____ Shots taken : _____

Power play goals : _____ Short handed goals : _____

Overtime goal : _____ Shoot out goal : _____ Game winning goal : ☐

Penalties : _____ Penality minutes : _____ +/- : _____ Hits : _____

Favorite game memory : _____
_____

Game Notes : _____
_____
_____
_____
_____
_____
_____
_____

FINAL SCORE			VISITOR
			HOME

Date : _____ **Hockey league level :** _____

City : _____

Arena : _____

My Team : _____

Opponent : _____

Position : _____ **Jersey Number :** _____

Goals : _____ **Assists :** _____ **Points :** _____ **Shots taken :** _____

Power play goals : _____ **Short handed goals :** _____

Overtime goal : _____ **Shoot out goal :** _____ **Game winning goal :** ☐

Penalties : _____ **Penality minutes :** _____ **+/- :** _____ **Hits :** _____

Favorite game memory : _____

_____

Game Notes : _____

_____

_____

_____

_____

_____

_____

_____

_____

48

FINAL SCORE			VISITOR
			HOME

Date : _____ Hockey league level : _____

City : _____

Arena : _____

My Team : _____

Opponent : _____

Position : _____ Jersey Number : _____

Goals : _____ Assists : _____ Points : _____ Shots taken : _____

Power play goals : _____ Short handed goals : _____

Overtime goal : _____ Shoot out goal : _____ Game winning goal : ☐

Penalties : _____ Penality minutes : _____ +/- : _____ Hits : _____

Favorite game memory : _____
_____

Game Notes : _____
_____
_____
_____
_____
_____
_____

FINAL SCORE			VISITOR
			HOME

Date : _____ **Hockey league level :** _____

City : _____

Arena : _____

My Team : _____

Opponent : _____

Position : _____ **Jersey Number :** _____

Goals : _____ **Assists :** _____ **Points :** _____ **Shots taken :** _____

Power play goals : _____ **Short handed goals :** _____

Overtime goal : _____ **Shoot out goal :** _____ **Game winning goal :** ☐

Penalties : _____ **Penality minutes :** _____ **+/- :** _____ **Hits :** _____

Favorite game memory : _____
_____

Game Notes : _____
_____
_____
_____
_____
_____
_____
_____
_____

50

FINAL SCORE			VISITOR	
			HOME	

Date : _____ Hockey league level : _____

City : _____

Arena : _____

My Team : _____

Opponent : _____

Position : _____ Jersey Number : _____

Goals : _____ Assists : _____ Points : _____ Shots taken : _____

Power play goals : _____ Short handed goals : _____

Overtime goal : _____ Shoot out goal : _____ Game winning goal : ☐

Penalties : _____ Penality minutes : _____ +/- : _____ Hits : _____

Favorite game memory : _____
_____

Game Notes : _____
_____
_____
_____
_____
_____
_____

FINAL SCORE			VISITOR
			HOME

Date : _____   Hockey league level : _____

City : _____

Arena : _____

My Team : _____

Opponent : _____

Position : _____   Jersey Number : _____

Goals : _____   Assists : _____   Points : _____   Shots taken : _____

Power play goals : _____   Short handed goals : _____

Overtime goal : _____   Shoot out goal : _____   Game winning goal : ☐

Penalties : _____   Penality minutes : _____   +/- : _____   Hits : _____

Favorite game memory : _____
_____

Game Notes : _____
_____
_____
_____
_____
_____
_____
_____

FINAL SCORE			VISITOR
			HOME

Date : _____ Hockey league level : _____

City : _____

Arena : _____

My Team : _____

Opponent : _____

Position : _____ Jersey Number : _____

Goals : _____ Assists : _____ Points : _____ Shots taken : _____

Power play goals : _____ Short handed goals : _____

Overtime goal : _____ Shoot out goal : _____ Game winning goal : ☐

Penalties : _____ Penality minutes : _____ +/- : _____ Hits : _____

Favorite game memory : _____

_____

Game Notes : _____

_____

_____

_____

_____

_____

_____

_____

FINAL SCORE			VISITOR
			HOME

Date : _____ **Hockey league level :** _____

City : _____

Arena : _____

My Team : _____

Opponent : _____

Position : _____ **Jersey Number :** _____

Goals : _____ **Assists :** _____ **Points :** _____ **Shots taken :** _____

Power play goals : _____ **Short handed goals :** _____

Overtime goal : _____ **Shoot out goal :** _____ **Game winning goal :** ☐

Penalties : _____ **Penality minutes :** _____ **+/- :** _____ **Hits :** _____

Favorite game memory : _____
_____

Game Notes : _____
_____
_____
_____
_____
_____
_____
_____

FINAL SCORE			VISITOR
			HOME

Date : _____ **Hockey league level :** _____

City : _____

Arena : _____

My Team : _____

Opponent : _____

Position : _____ **Jersey Number :** _____

Goals : _____ **Assists :** _____ **Points :** _____ **Shots taken :** _____

Power play goals : _____ **Short handed goals :** _____

Overtime goal : _____ **Shoot out goal :** _____ **Game winning goal :** ☐

Penalties : _____ **Penality minutes :** _____ **+/- :** _____ **Hits :** _____

Favorite game memory : _____
_____

Game Notes : _____
_____
_____
_____
_____
_____
_____
_____

55

FINAL SCORE			VISITOR
			HOME

Date : _____ **Hockey league level :** _____

City : _____

Arena : _____

My Team : _____

Opponent : _____

Position : _____ **Jersey Number :** _____

Goals : _____ **Assists :** _____ **Points :** _____ **Shots taken :** _____

Power play goals : _____ **Short handed goals :** _____

Overtime goal : _____ **Shoot out goal :** _____ **Game winning goal :** ☐

Penalties : _____ **Penality minutes :** _____ **+/- :** _____ **Hits :** _____

Favorite game memory : _____
_____

Game Notes : _____
_____
_____
_____
_____
_____
_____
_____

FINAL SCORE			VISITOR
			HOME

Date : _____ **Hockey league level :** _____

City : _____

Arena : _____

My Team : _____

Opponent : _____

Position : _____ **Jersey Number :** _____

Goals : _____ **Assists :** _____ **Points :** _____ **Shots taken :** _____

Power play goals : _____ **Short handed goals :** _____

Overtime goal : _____ **Shoot out goal :** _____ **Game winning goal :** ☐

Penalties : _____ **Penality minutes :** _____ **+/- :** _____ **Hits :** _____

Favorite game memory : _____

Game Notes : _____

FINAL SCORE			VISITOR
			HOME

Date : _____ Hockey league level : _____

City : _____

Arena : _____

My Team : _____

Opponent : _____

Position : _____ Jersey Number : _____

Goals : _____ Assists : _____ Points : _____ Shots taken : _____

Power play goals : _____ Short handed goals : _____

Overtime goal : _____ Shoot out goal : _____ Game winning goal : ☐

Penalties : _____ Penality minutes : _____ +/- : _____ Hits : _____

Favorite game memory : _____
_____

Game Notes : _____
_____
_____
_____
_____
_____
_____
_____
_____

FINAL SCORE			VISITOR
			HOME

Date : _____ Hockey league level : _____

City : _____

Arena : _____

My Team : _____

Opponent : _____

Position : _____ Jersey Number : _____

Goals : _____ Assists : _____ Points : _____ Shots taken : _____

Power play goals : _____ Short handed goals : _____

Overtime goal : _____ Shoot out goal : _____ Game winning goal : ☐

Penalties : _____ Penality minutes : _____ +/- : _____ Hits : _____

Favorite game memory : _____
_____

Game Notes : _____
_____
_____
_____
_____
_____
_____
_____

FINAL SCORE			VISITOR
			HOME

Date : _____ Hockey league level : _____

City : _____

Arena : _____

My Team : _____

Opponent : _____

Position : _____ Jersey Number : _____

Goals : _____ Assists : _____ Points : _____ Shots taken : _____

Power play goals : _____ Short handed goals : _____

Overtime goal : _____ Shoot out goal : _____ Game winning goal : ☐

Penalties : _____ Penality minutes : _____ +/- : _____ Hits : _____

Favorite game memory : _____
_____

Game Notes : _____
_____
_____
_____
_____
_____
_____
_____

FINAL SCORE			VISITOR
			HOME

Date : _____ Hockey league level : _____

City : _____

Arena : _____

My Team : _____

Opponent : _____

Position : _____ Jersey Number : _____

Goals : _____ Assists : _____ Points : _____ Shots taken : _____

Power play goals : _____ Short handed goals : _____

Overtime goal : _____ Shoot out goal : _____ Game winning goal : ☐

Penalties : _____ Penality minutes : _____ +/- : _____ Hits : _____

Favorite game memory : _____
_____

Game Notes : _____
_____
_____
_____
_____
_____
_____

FINAL SCORE			VISITOR
			HOME

Date : _____ Hockey league level : _____

City : _____

Arena : _____

My Team : _____

Opponent : _____

Position : _____ Jersey Number : _____

Goals : _____ Assists : _____ Points : _____ Shots taken : _____

Power play goals : _____ Short handed goals : _____

Overtime goal : _____ Shoot out goal : _____ Game winning goal : ☐

Penalties : _____ Penality minutes : _____ +/- : _____ Hits : _____

Favorite game memory : _____

_____

Game Notes : _____

_____

_____

_____

_____

_____

_____

_____

FINAL SCORE			VISITOR
			HOME

Date : _____ Hockey league level : _____

City : _____

Arena : _____

My Team : _____

Opponent : _____

Position : _____ Jersey Number : _____

Goals : _____ Assists : _____ Points : _____ Shots taken : _____

Power play goals : _____ Short handed goals : _____

Overtime goal : _____ Shoot out goal : _____ Game winning goal : ☐

Penalties : _____ Penality minutes : _____ +/- : _____ Hits : _____

Favorite game memory : _____

_____

Game Notes : _____

_____

_____

_____

_____

_____

_____

_____

_____

FINAL SCORE			VISITOR
			HOME

Date : _____ Hockey league level : _____

City : _____

Arena : _____

My Team : _____

Opponent : _____

Position : _____ Jersey Number : _____

Goals : _____ Assists : _____ Points : _____ Shots taken : _____

Power play goals : _____ Short handed goals : _____

Overtime goal : _____ Shoot out goal : _____ Game winning goal : ☐

Penalties : _____ Penality minutes : _____ +/- : _____ Hits : _____

Favorite game memory : _____
_____

Game Notes : _____
_____
_____
_____
_____
_____
_____
_____

FINAL SCORE			VISITOR
			HOME

Date : _____ **Hockey league level :** _____

City : _____

Arena : _____

My Team : _____

Opponent : _____

Position : _____ **Jersey Number :** _____

Goals : _____ **Assists :** _____ **Points :** _____ **Shots taken :** _____

Power play goals : _____ **Short handed goals :** _____

Overtime goal : _____ **Shoot out goal :** _____ **Game winning goal :** ☐

Penalties : _____ **Penality minutes :** _____ **+/- :** _____ **Hits :** _____

Favorite game memory : _____

Game Notes : _____

FINAL SCORE			VISITOR
			HOME

Date : _____ Hockey league level : _____

City : _____

Arena : _____

My Team : _____

Opponent : _____

Position : _____ Jersey Number : _____

Goals : _____ Assists : _____ Points : _____ Shots taken : _____

Power play goals : _____ Short handed goals : _____

Overtime goal : _____ Shoot out goal : _____ Game winning goal : ☐

Penalties : _____ Penality minutes : _____ +/- : _____ Hits : _____

Favorite game memory : _____
_____

Game Notes : _____
_____
_____
_____
_____
_____
_____
_____

FINAL SCORE			VISITOR
			HOME

Date : _____ Hockey league level : _____

City : _____

Arena : _____

My Team : _____

Opponent : _____

Position : _____ Jersey Number : _____

Goals : _____ Assists : _____ Points : _____ Shots taken : _____

Power play goals : _____ Short handed goals : _____

Overtime goal : _____ Shoot out goal : _____ Game winning goal : ☐

Penalties : _____ Penality minutes : _____ +/- : _____ Hits : _____

Favorite game memory : _____
_____

Game Notes : _____
_____
_____
_____
_____
_____
_____
_____

FINAL SCORE			VISITOR
			HOME

Date : _____ Hockey league level : _____

City : _____

Arena : _____

My Team : _____

Opponent : _____

Position : _____ Jersey Number : _____

Goals : _____ Assists : _____ Points : _____ Shots taken : _____

Power play goals : _____ Short handed goals : _____

Overtime goal : _____ Shoot out goal : _____ Game winning goal : ☐

Penalties : _____ Penality minutes : _____ +/- : _____ Hits : _____

Favorite game memory : _____
_____

Game Notes : _____
_____
_____
_____
_____
_____
_____
_____

FINAL SCORE			VISITOR
			HOME

Date : _____ Hockey league level : _____

City : _____

Arena : _____

My Team : _____

Opponent : _____

Position : _____ Jersey Number : _____

Goals : _____ Assists : _____ Points : _____ Shots taken : _____

Power play goals : _____ Short handed goals : _____

Overtime goal : _____ Shoot out goal : _____ Game winning goal : ☐

Penalties : _____ Penality minutes : _____ +/- : _____ Hits : _____

Favorite game memory : _____
_____

Game Notes : _____
_____
_____
_____
_____
_____
_____
_____

FINAL SCORE			VISITOR
			HOME

Date : _____ Hockey league level : _____

City : _____

Arena : _____

My Team : _____

Opponent : _____

Position : _____ Jersey Number : _____

Goals : _____ Assists : _____ Points : _____ Shots taken : _____

Power play goals : _____ Short handed goals : _____

Overtime goal : _____ Shoot out goal : _____ Game winning goal : ☐

Penalties : _____ Penality minutes : _____ +/- : _____ Hits : _____

Favorite game memory : _____

_____

Game Notes : _____

_____

_____

_____

_____

_____

_____

_____

_____

FINAL SCORE			VISITOR
			HOME

Date : _____ Hockey league level : _____

City : _____

Arena : _____

My Team : _____

Opponent : _____

Position : _____ Jersey Number : _____

Goals : _____ Assists : _____ Points : _____ Shots taken : _____

Power play goals : _____ Short handed goals : _____

Overtime goal : _____ Shoot out goal : _____ Game winning goal : ☐

Penalties : _____ Penality minutes : _____ +/- : _____ Hits : _____

Favorite game memory : _____
_____

Game Notes : _____
_____
_____
_____
_____
_____
_____
_____

FINAL SCORE			VISITOR
			HOME

Date : _____ Hockey league level : _____

City : _____

Arena : _____

My Team : _____

Opponent : _____

Position : _____ Jersey Number : _____

Goals : _____ Assists : _____ Points : _____ Shots taken : _____

Power play goals : _____ Short handed goals : _____

Overtime goal : _____ Shoot out goal : _____ Game winning goal : ☐

Penalties : _____ Penality minutes : _____ +/- : _____ Hits : _____

Favorite game memory : _____
_____

Game Notes : _____
_____
_____
_____
_____
_____
_____
_____

FINAL SCORE			VISITOR
			HOME

Date : _____   Hockey league level : _____

City : _____

Arena : _____

My Team : _____

Opponent : _____

Position : _____   Jersey Number : _____

Goals : _____   Assists : _____   Points : _____   Shots taken : _____

Power play goals : _____   Short handed goals : _____

Overtime goal : _____   Shoot out goal : _____   Game winning goal : ☐

Penalties : _____   Penality minutes : _____   +/- : _____   Hits : _____

Favorite game memory : _____
_____

Game Notes : _____
_____
_____
_____
_____
_____
_____
_____

73

FINAL SCORE			VISITOR
			HOME

Date : _____ Hockey league level : _____

City : _____

Arena : _____

My Team : _____

Opponent : _____

Position : _____ Jersey Number : _____

Goals : _____ Assists : _____ Points : _____ Shots taken : _____

Power play goals : _____ Short handed goals : _____

Overtime goal : _____ Shoot out goal : _____ Game winning goal : ☐

Penalties : _____ Penality minutes : _____ +/- : _____ Hits : _____

Favorite game memory : _____
_____

Game Notes : _____
_____
_____
_____
_____
_____
_____
_____

FINAL SCORE			VISITOR
			HOME

Date : _____ Hockey league level : _____

City : _____

Arena : _____

My Team : _____

Opponent : _____

Position : _____ Jersey Number : _____

Goals : _____ Assists : _____ Points : _____ Shots taken : _____

Power play goals : _____ Short handed goals : _____

Overtime goal : _____ Shoot out goal : _____ Game winning goal : ☐

Penalties : _____ Penality minutes : _____ +/- : _____ Hits : _____

Favorite game memory : _____
_____

Game Notes : _____
_____
_____
_____
_____
_____
_____

75

FINAL SCORE			VISITOR
			HOME

Date : _____ **Hockey league level :** _____

City : _____

Arena : _____

My Team : _____

Opponent : _____

Position : _____ **Jersey Number :** _____

Goals : _____ **Assists :** _____ **Points :** _____ **Shots taken :** _____

Power play goals : _____ **Short handed goals :** _____

Overtime goal : _____ **Shoot out goal :** _____ **Game winning goal :** ☐

Penalties : _____ **Penality minutes :** _____ **+/- :** _____ **Hits :** _____

Favorite game memory : _____
_____

Game Notes : _____
_____
_____
_____
_____
_____
_____
_____

FINAL SCORE			**VISITOR**
			HOME

Date : _____ **Hockey league level :** _____

City : _____

Arena : _____

My Team : _____

Opponent : _____

Position : _____ **Jersey Number :** _____

Goals : _____ **Assists :** _____ **Points :** _____ **Shots taken :** _____

Power play goals : _____ **Short handed goals :** _____

Overtime goal : _____ **Shoot out goal :** _____ **Game winning goal :** ☐

Penalties : _____ **Penality minutes :** _____ **+/- :** _____ **Hits :** _____

Favorite game memory : _____

_____

Game Notes : _____

_____

_____

_____

_____

_____

_____

_____

FINAL SCORE			VISITOR
			HOME

Date : _____ Hockey league level : _____

City : _____

Arena : _____

My Team : _____

Opponent : _____

Position : _____ Jersey Number : _____

Goals : _____ Assists : _____ Points : _____ Shots taken : _____

Power play goals : _____ Short handed goals : _____

Overtime goal : _____ Shoot out goal : _____ Game winning goal : ☐

Penalties : _____ Penality minutes : _____ +/- : _____ Hits : _____

Favorite game memory : _____
_____

Game Notes : _____
_____
_____
_____
_____
_____
_____
_____

FINAL SCORE			VISITOR
			HOME

Date : _____ **Hockey league level :** _____

City : _____

Arena : _____

My Team : _____

Opponent : _____

Position : _____ **Jersey Number :** _____

Goals : _____ **Assists :** _____ **Points :** _____ **Shots taken :** _____

Power play goals : _____ **Short handed goals :** _____

Overtime goal : _____ **Shoot out goal :** _____ **Game winning goal :** ☐

Penalties : _____ **Penality minutes :** _____ **+/- :** _____ **Hits :** _____

Favorite game memory : _____
_____

Game Notes : _____
_____
_____
_____
_____
_____
_____
_____

FINAL SCORE			VISITOR
			HOME

Date : _____ Hockey league level : _____

City : _____

Arena : _____

My Team : _____

Opponent : _____

Position : _____ Jersey Number : _____

Goals : _____ Assists : _____ Points : _____ Shots taken : _____

Power play goals : _____ Short handed goals : _____

Overtime goal : _____ Shoot out goal : _____ Game winning goal : ☐

Penalties : _____ Penality minutes : _____ +/- : _____ Hits : _____

Favorite game memory : _____
_____

Game Notes : _____
_____
_____
_____
_____
_____
_____
_____

FINAL SCORE			VISITOR
			HOME

Date : _____ Hockey league level : _____

City : _____

Arena : _____

My Team : _____

Opponent : _____

Position : _____ Jersey Number : _____

Goals : _____ Assists : _____ Points : _____ Shots taken : _____

Power play goals : _____ Short handed goals : _____

Overtime goal : _____ Shoot out goal : _____ Game winning goal : ☐

Penalties : _____ Penality minutes : _____ +/- : _____ Hits : _____

Favorite game memory : _____
_____

Game Notes : _____
_____
_____
_____
_____
_____
_____
_____

FINAL SCORE			VISITOR
			HOME

Date : _____ Hockey league level : _____

City : _____

Arena : _____

My Team : _____

Opponent : _____

Position : _____ Jersey Number : _____

Goals : _____ Assists : _____ Points : _____ Shots taken : _____

Power play goals : _____ Short handed goals : _____

Overtime goal : _____ Shoot out goal : _____ Game winning goal : ☐

Penalties : _____ Penality minutes : _____ +/- : _____ Hits : _____

Favorite game memory : _____
_____

Game Notes : _____
_____
_____
_____
_____
_____
_____
_____

FINAL SCORE			VISITOR
			HOME

Date : _____ Hockey league level : _____

City : _____

Arena : _____

My Team : _____

Opponent : _____

Position : _____ Jersey Number : _____

Goals : _____ Assists : _____ Points : _____ Shots taken : _____

Power play goals : _____ Short handed goals : _____

Overtime goal : _____ Shoot out goal : _____ Game winning goal : ☐

Penalties : _____ Penality minutes : _____ +/- : _____ Hits : _____

Favorite game memory : _____
_____

Game Notes : _____
_____
_____
_____
_____
_____
_____
_____

FINAL SCORE			VISITOR
			HOME

Date : _____ Hockey league level : _____

City : _____

Arena : _____

My Team : _____

Opponent : _____

Position : _____ Jersey Number : _____

Goals : _____ Assists : _____ Points : _____ Shots taken : _____

Power play goals : _____ Short handed goals : _____

Overtime goal : _____ Shoot out goal : _____ Game winning goal : ☐

Penalties : _____ Penality minutes : _____ +/- : _____ Hits : _____

Favorite game memory : _____
_____

Game Notes : _____
_____
_____
_____
_____
_____
_____
_____
_____

FINAL SCORE			VISITOR
			HOME

Date : _____ Hockey league level : _____

City : _____

Arena : _____

My Team : _____

Opponent : _____

Position : _____ Jersey Number : _____

Goals : _____ Assists : _____ Points : _____ Shots taken : _____

Power play goals : _____ Short handed goals : _____

Overtime goal : _____ Shoot out goal : _____ Game winning goal : ☐

Penalties : _____ Penality minutes : _____ +/- : _____ Hits : _____

Favorite game memory : _____
_____

Game Notes : _____
_____
_____
_____
_____
_____
_____
_____

FINAL SCORE			VISITOR
			HOME

Date : _____ **Hockey league level :** _____

City : _____

Arena : _____

My Team : _____

Opponent : _____

Position : _____ **Jersey Number :** _____

Goals : _____ **Assists :** _____ **Points :** _____ **Shots taken :** _____

Power play goals : _____ **Short handed goals :** _____

Overtime goal : _____ **Shoot out goal :** _____ **Game winning goal :** ☐

Penalties : _____ **Penality minutes :** _____ **+/- :** _____ **Hits :** _____

Favorite game memory : _____
_____

Game Notes : _____
_____
_____
_____
_____
_____
_____
_____

FINAL SCORE			VISITOR
			HOME

Date : _____ **Hockey league level :** _____

City : _____

Arena : _____

My Team : _____

Opponent : _____

Position : _____ **Jersey Number :** _____

Goals : _____ **Assists :** _____ **Points :** _____ **Shots taken :** _____

Power play goals : _____ **Short handed goals :** _____

Overtime goal : _____ **Shoot out goal :** _____ **Game winning goal :** ☐

Penalties : _____ **Penality minutes :** _____ **+/- :** _____ **Hits :** _____

Favorite game memory : _____
_____

Game Notes : _____
_____
_____
_____
_____
_____
_____
_____

FINAL SCORE			VISITOR
			HOME

Date : _____ Hockey league level : _____

City : _____

Arena : _____

My Team : _____

Opponent : _____

Position : _____ Jersey Number : _____

Goals : _____ Assists : _____ Points : _____ Shots taken : _____

Power play goals : _____ Short handed goals : _____

Overtime goal : _____ Shoot out goal : _____ Game winning goal : ☐

Penalties : _____ Penality minutes : _____ +/- : _____ Hits : _____

Favorite game memory : _____
_____

Game Notes : _____
_____
_____
_____
_____
_____
_____
_____

FINAL SCORE			VISITOR
			HOME

Date : _____ Hockey league level : _____

City : _____

Arena : _____

My Team : _____

Opponent : _____

Position : _____ Jersey Number : _____

Goals : _____ Assists : _____ Points : _____ Shots taken : _____

Power play goals : _____ Short handed goals : _____

Overtime goal : _____ Shoot out goal : _____ Game winning goal : ☐

Penalties : _____ Penality minutes : _____ +/- : _____ Hits : _____

Favorite game memory : _____
_____

Game Notes : _____
_____
_____
_____
_____
_____
_____
_____
_____

FINAL SCORE			VISITOR
			HOME

Date : _____ Hockey league level : _____

City : _____

Arena : _____

My Team : _____

Opponent : _____

Position : _____ Jersey Number : _____

Goals : _____ Assists : _____ Points : _____ Shots taken : _____

Power play goals : _____ Short handed goals : _____

Overtime goal : _____ Shoot out goal : _____ Game winning goal : ☐

Penalties : _____ Penality minutes : _____ +/- : _____ Hits : _____

Favorite game memory : _____
_____

Game Notes : _____
_____
_____
_____
_____
_____
_____
_____

FINAL SCORE			VISITOR
			HOME

Date : _____ **Hockey league level :** _____

City : _____

Arena : _____

My Team : _____

Opponent : _____

Position : _____ **Jersey Number :** _____

Goals : _____ **Assists :** _____ **Points :** _____ **Shots taken :** _____

Power play goals : _____ **Short handed goals :** _____

Overtime goal : _____ **Shoot out goal :** _____ **Game winning goal :** ☐

Penalties : _____ **Penality minutes :** _____ **+/- :** _____ **Hits :** _____

Favorite game memory : _____

_____

Game Notes : _____

_____

_____

_____

_____

_____

_____

_____

FINAL SCORE			VISITOR
			HOME

Date : _____ **Hockey league level :** _____

City : _____

Arena : _____

My Team : _____

Opponent : _____

Position : _____ **Jersey Number :** _____

Goals : _____ **Assists :** _____ **Points :** _____ **Shots taken :** _____

Power play goals : _____ **Short handed goals :** _____

Overtime goal : _____ **Shoot out goal :** _____ **Game winning goal :** ☐

Penalties : _____ **Penality minutes :** _____ **+/- :** _____ **Hits :** _____

Favorite game memory : _____
_____

Game Notes : _____
_____
_____
_____
_____
_____
_____
_____

FINAL SCORE			VISITOR
			HOME

Date : _____ Hockey league level : _____

City : _____

Arena : _____

My Team : _____

Opponent : _____

Position : _____ Jersey Number : _____

Goals : _____ Assists : _____ Points : _____ Shots taken : _____

Power play goals : _____ Short handed goals : _____

Overtime goal : _____ Shoot out goal : _____ Game winning goal : ☐

Penalties : _____ Penality minutes : _____ +/- : _____ Hits : _____

Favorite game memory : _____
_____

Game Notes : _____
_____
_____
_____
_____
_____
_____
_____

FINAL SCORE			VISITOR
			HOME

Date : _____   Hockey league level : _____

City : _____

Arena : _____

My Team : _____

Opponent : _____

Position : _____   Jersey Number : _____

Goals : _____ Assists : _____ Points : _____ Shots taken : _____

Power play goals : _____ Short handed goals : _____

Overtime goal : _____ Shoot out goal : _____ Game winning goal : ☐

Penalties : _____ Penality minutes : _____ +/- : _____ Hits : _____

Favorite game memory : _____
_____

Game Notes : _____
_____
_____
_____
_____
_____
_____
_____

FINAL SCORE			VISITOR
			HOME

Date : _____ Hockey league level : _____

City : _____

Arena : _____

My Team : _____

Opponent : _____

Position : _____ Jersey Number : _____

Goals : _____ Assists : _____ Points : _____ Shots taken : _____

Power play goals : _____ Short handed goals : _____

Overtime goal : _____ Shoot out goal : _____ Game winning goal : ☐

Penalties : _____ Penality minutes : _____ +/- : _____ Hits : _____

Favorite game memory : _____

_____

Game Notes : _____

_____

_____

_____

_____

_____

_____

_____

_____

FINAL SCORE			VISITOR
			HOME

Date : _____ **Hockey league level :** _____

City : _____

Arena : _____

My Team : _____

Opponent : _____

Position : _____ **Jersey Number :** _____

Goals : _____ **Assists :** _____ **Points :** _____ **Shots taken :** _____

Power play goals : _____ **Short handed goals :** _____

Overtime goal : _____ **Shoot out goal :** _____ **Game winning goal :** ☐

Penalties : _____ **Penality minutes :** _____ **+/- :** _____ **Hits :** _____

Favorite game memory : _____

_____

Game Notes : _____

_____

_____

_____

_____

_____

_____

_____

FINAL SCORE			**VISITOR**
			HOME

Date : _____ Hockey league level : _____

City : _____

Arena : _____

My Team : _____

Opponent : _____

Position : _____ Jersey Number : _____

Goals : _____ Assists : _____ Points : _____ Shots taken : _____

Power play goals : _____ Short handed goals : _____

Overtime goal : _____ Shoot out goal : _____ Game winning goal : ☐

Penalties : _____ Penality minutes : _____ +/- : _____ Hits : _____

Favorite game memory : _____
_____

Game Notes : _____
_____
_____
_____
_____
_____
_____
_____

FINAL SCORE			VISITOR
			HOME

Date : _____ Hockey league level : _____

City : _____

Arena : _____

My Team : _____

Opponent : _____

Position : _____ Jersey Number : _____

Goals : _____ Assists : _____ Points : _____ Shots taken : _____

Power play goals : _____ Short handed goals : _____

Overtime goal : _____ Shoot out goal : _____ Game winning goal : ☐

Penalties : _____ Penality minutes : _____ +/- : _____ Hits : _____

Favorite game memory : _____
_____

Game Notes : _____
_____
_____
_____
_____
_____
_____
_____

FINAL SCORE			VISITOR
			HOME

Date : _____ Hockey league level : _____

City : _____

Arena : _____

My Team : _____

Opponent : _____

Position : _____ Jersey Number : _____

Goals : _____ Assists : _____ Points : _____ Shots taken : _____

Power play goals : _____ Short handed goals : _____

Overtime goal : _____ Shoot out goal : _____ Game winning goal : ☐

Penalties : _____ Penality minutes : _____ +/- : _____ Hits : _____

Favorite game memory : _____
_____

Game Notes : _____
_____
_____
_____
_____
_____
_____

FINAL SCORE			VISITOR
			HOME

Date : _____ Hockey league level : _____

City : _____

Arena : _____

My Team : _____

Opponent : _____

Position : _____ Jersey Number : _____

Goals : _____ Assists : _____ Points : _____ Shots taken : _____

Power play goals : _____ Short handed goals : _____

Overtime goal : _____ Shoot out goal : _____ Game winning goal : ☐

Penalties : _____ Penality minutes : _____ +/- : _____ Hits : _____

Favorite game memory : _____
_____

Game Notes : _____
_____
_____
_____
_____
_____
_____
_____
_____

FINAL SCORE			VISITOR
			HOME

Date : _____ **Hockey league level :** _____

City : _____

Arena : _____

My Team : _____

Opponent : _____

Position : _____ **Jersey Number :** _____

Goals : _____ **Assists :** _____ **Points :** _____ **Shots taken :** _____

Power play goals : _____ **Short handed goals :** _____

Overtime goal : _____ **Shoot out goal :** _____ **Game winning goal :** ☐

Penalties : _____ **Penality minutes :** _____ **+/- :** _____ **Hits :** _____

Favorite game memory : _____
_____

Game Notes : _____
_____
_____
_____
_____
_____
_____
_____

FINAL SCORE			VISITOR
			HOME

Date : _____ Hockey league level : _____

City : _____

Arena : _____

My Team : _____

Opponent : _____

Position : _____ Jersey Number : _____

Goals : _____ Assists : _____ Points : _____ Shots taken : _____

Power play goals : _____ Short handed goals : _____

Overtime goal : _____ Shoot out goal : _____ Game winning goal : ☐

Penalties : _____ Penality minutes : _____ +/- : _____ Hits : _____

Favorite game memory : _____

_____

Game Notes : _____

_____

_____

_____

_____

_____

_____

_____

FINAL SCORE			VISITOR
			HOME

Date : _____ **Hockey league level :** _____

City : _____

Arena : _____

My Team : _____

Opponent : _____

Position : _____ **Jersey Number :** _____

Goals : _____ **Assists :** _____ **Points :** _____ **Shots taken :** _____

Power play goals : _____ **Short handed goals :** _____

Overtime goal : _____ **Shoot out goal :** _____ **Game winning goal :** ☐

Penalties : _____ **Penality minutes :** _____ **+/- :** _____ **Hits :** _____

Favorite game memory : _____
_____

Game Notes : _____
_____
_____
_____
_____
_____
_____
_____

FINAL SCORE			VISITOR
			HOME

Date : _____ Hockey league level : _____

City : _____

Arena : _____

My Team : _____

Opponent : _____

Position : _____ Jersey Number : _____

Goals : _____ Assists : _____ Points : _____ Shots taken : _____

Power play goals : _____ Short handed goals : _____

Overtime goal : _____ Shoot out goal : _____ Game winning goal : ☐

Penalties : _____ Penality minutes : _____ +/- : _____ Hits : _____

Favorite game memory : _____

_____

Game Notes : _____

_____

_____

_____

_____

_____

_____

FINAL SCORE			VISITOR
			HOME

Date : _____ Hockey league level : _____

City : _____

Arena : _____

My Team : _____

Opponent : _____

Position : _____ Jersey Number : _____

Goals : _____ Assists : _____ Points : _____ Shots taken : _____

Power play goals : _____ Short handed goals : _____

Overtime goal : _____ Shoot out goal : _____ Game winning goal : ☐

Penalties : _____ Penality minutes : _____ +/- : _____ Hits : _____

Favorite game memory : _____
_____

Game Notes : _____
_____
_____
_____
_____
_____
_____
_____

FINAL SCORE			VISITOR
			HOME

Date : _____ Hockey league level : _____

City : _____

Arena : _____

My Team : _____

Opponent : _____

Position : _____ Jersey Number : _____

Goals : _____ Assists : _____ Points : _____ Shots taken : _____

Power play goals : _____ Short handed goals : _____

Overtime goal : _____ Shoot out goal : _____ Game winning goal : ☐

Penalties : _____ Penality minutes : _____ +/- : _____ Hits : _____

Favorite game memory : _____
_____

Game Notes : _____
_____
_____
_____
_____
_____
_____
_____

FINAL SCORE			VISITOR
			HOME

Date : _____ Hockey league level : _____

City : _____

Arena : _____

My Team : _____

Opponent : _____

Position : _____ Jersey Number : _____

Goals : _____ Assists : _____ Points : _____ Shots taken : _____

Power play goals : _____ Short handed goals : _____

Overtime goal : _____ Shoot out goal : _____ Game winning goal : ☐

Penalties : _____ Penality minutes : _____ +/- : _____ Hits : _____

Favorite game memory : _____
_____

Game Notes : _____
_____
_____
_____
_____
_____
_____
_____

FINAL SCORE			VISITOR
			HOME

Date : _____   **Hockey league level :** _____

City : _____

Arena : _____

My Team : _____

Opponent : _____

Position : _____   **Jersey Number :** _____

Goals : _____   **Assists :** _____   **Points :** _____   **Shots taken :** _____

Power play goals : _____   **Short handed goals :** _____

Overtime goal : _____   **Shoot out goal :** _____   **Game winning goal :** ☐

Penalties : _____   **Penality minutes :** _____   **+/- :** _____   **Hits :** _____

Favorite game memory : _____
_____

Game Notes : _____
_____
_____
_____
_____
_____
_____
_____

FINAL SCORE			VISITOR
			HOME

Date : _____ Hockey league level : _____

City : _____

Arena : _____

My Team : _____

Opponent : _____

Position : _____ Jersey Number : _____

Goals : _____ Assists : _____ Points : _____ Shots taken : _____

Power play goals : _____ Short handed goals : _____

Overtime goal : _____ Shoot out goal : _____ Game winning goal : ☐

Penalties : _____ Penality minutes : _____ +/- : _____ Hits : _____

Favorite game memory : _____
_____

Game Notes : _____
_____
_____
_____
_____
_____
_____
_____

FINAL SCORE			VISITOR
			HOME

Date : _____ Hockey league level : _____

City : _____

Arena : _____

My Team : _____

Opponent : _____

Position : _____ Jersey Number : _____

Goals : _____ Assists : _____ Points : _____ Shots taken : _____

Power play goals : _____ Short handed goals : _____

Overtime goal : _____ Shoot out goal : _____ Game winning goal : ☐

Penalties : _____ Penality minutes : _____ +/- : _____ Hits : _____

Favorite game memory : _____
_____

Game Notes : _____
_____
_____
_____
_____
_____
_____
_____

FINAL SCORE			VISITOR
			HOME

Date : _____ **Hockey league level :** _____

City : _____

Arena : _____

My Team : _____

Opponent : _____

Position : _____ **Jersey Number :** _____

Goals : _____ **Assists :** _____ **Points :** _____ **Shots taken :** _____

Power play goals : _____ **Short handed goals :** _____

Overtime goal : _____ **Shoot out goal :** _____ **Game winning goal :** ☐

Penalties : _____ **Penality minutes :** _____ **+/- :** _____ **Hits :** _____

Favorite game memory : _____
_____

Game Notes : _____
_____
_____
_____
_____
_____
_____
_____

FINAL SCORE			VISITOR
			HOME

Date : _____ Hockey league level : _____

City : _____

Arena : _____

My Team : _____

Opponent : _____

Position : _____ Jersey Number : _____

Goals : _____ Assists : _____ Points : _____ Shots taken : _____

Power play goals : _____ Short handed goals : _____

Overtime goal : _____ Shoot out goal : _____ Game winning goal : ☐

Penalties : _____ Penality minutes : _____ +/- : _____ Hits : _____

Favorite game memory : _____
_____

Game Notes : _____
_____
_____
_____
_____
_____
_____
_____

FINAL SCORE			VISITOR
			HOME

Date : _____ Hockey league level : _____

City : _____

Arena : _____

My Team : _____

Opponent : _____

Position : _____ Jersey Number : _____

Goals : _____ Assists : _____ Points : _____ Shots taken : _____

Power play goals : _____ Short handed goals : _____

Overtime goal : _____ Shoot out goal : _____ Game winning goal : ☐

Penalties : _____ Penality minutes : _____ +/- : _____ Hits : _____

Favorite game memory : _____

_____

Game Notes : _____

_____

_____

_____

_____

_____

_____

_____

FINAL SCORE			VISITOR
			HOME

Date : _____ Hockey league level : _____

City : _____

Arena : _____

My Team : _____

Opponent : _____

Position : _____ Jersey Number : _____

Goals : _____ Assists : _____ Points : _____ Shots taken : _____

Power play goals : _____ Short handed goals : _____

Overtime goal : _____ Shoot out goal : _____ Game winning goal : ☐

Penalties : _____ Penality minutes : _____ +/- : _____ Hits : _____

Favorite game memory : _____

Game Notes : _____

FINAL SCORE			VISITOR
			HOME

Date : _____ Hockey league level : _____

City : _____

Arena : _____

My Team : _____

Opponent : _____

Position : _____ Jersey Number : _____

Goals : _____ Assists : _____ Points : _____ Shots taken : _____

Power play goals : _____ Short handed goals : _____

Overtime goal : _____ Shoot out goal : _____ Game winning goal : ☐

Penalties : _____ Penality minutes : _____ +/- : _____ Hits : _____

Favorite game memory : _____
_____

Game Notes : _____
_____
_____
_____
_____
_____
_____
_____

115

FINAL SCORE			VISITOR
			HOME

Date : _____ Hockey league level : _____

City : _____

Arena : _____

My Team : _____

Opponent : _____

Position : _____ Jersey Number : _____

Goals : _____ Assists : _____ Points : _____ Shots taken : _____

Power play goals : _____ Short handed goals : _____

Overtime goal : _____ Shoot out goal : _____ Game winning goal : ☐

Penalties : _____ Penality minutes : _____ +/- : _____ Hits : _____

Favorite game memory : _____
_____

Game Notes : _____
_____
_____
_____
_____
_____
_____

FINAL SCORE			VISITOR
			HOME

Date : _____ **Hockey league level :** _____

City : _____

Arena : _____

My Team : _____

Opponent : _____

Position : _____ **Jersey Number :** _____

Goals : _____ **Assists :** _____ **Points :** _____ **Shots taken :** _____

Power play goals : _____ **Short handed goals :** _____

Overtime goal : _____ **Shoot out goal :** _____ **Game winning goal :** ☐

Penalties : _____ **Penality minutes :** _____ **+/- :** _____ **Hits :** _____

Favorite game memory : _____
_____

Game Notes : _____
_____
_____
_____
_____
_____
_____

FINAL SCORE			VISITOR
			HOME

Date : _____ **Hockey league level :** _____

City : _____

Arena : _____

My Team : _____

Opponent : _____

Position : _____ **Jersey Number :** _____

Goals : _____ **Assists :** _____ **Points :** _____ **Shots taken :** _____

Power play goals : _____ **Short handed goals :** _____

Overtime goal : _____ **Shoot out goal :** _____ **Game winning goal :** ☐

Penalties : _____ **Penality minutes :** _____ **+/- :** _____ **Hits :** _____

Favorite game memory : _____
_____

Game Notes : _____
_____
_____
_____
_____
_____
_____

FINAL SCORE			VISITOR
			HOME

Date : _____   Hockey league level : _____

City : _____

Arena : _____

My Team : _____

Opponent : _____

Position : _____   Jersey Number : _____

Goals : _____   Assists : _____   Points : _____   Shots taken : _____

Power play goals : _____   Short handed goals : _____

Overtime goal : _____   Shoot out goal : _____   Game winning goal : ☐

Penalties : _____   Penality minutes : _____   +/- : _____   Hits : _____

Favorite game memory : _____
_____

Game Notes : _____
_____
_____
_____
_____
_____
_____
_____

FINAL SCORE			VISITOR
			HOME

Date : _____ Hockey league level : _____

City : _____

Arena : _____

My Team : _____

Opponent : _____

Position : _____ Jersey Number : _____

Goals : _____ Assists : _____ Points : _____ Shots taken : _____

Power play goals : _____ Short handed goals : _____

Overtime goal : _____ Shoot out goal : _____ Game winning goal : ☐

Penalties : _____ Penality minutes : _____ +/- : _____ Hits : _____

Favorite game memory : _____
_____

Game Notes : _____
_____
_____
_____
_____
_____
_____

FINAL SCORE			VISITOR
			HOME

Date : _____   Hockey league level : _____

City : _____

Arena : _____

My Team : _____

Opponent : _____

Position : _____   Jersey Number : _____

Goals : _____   Assists : _____   Points : _____   Shots taken : _____

Power play goals : _____   Short handed goals : _____

Overtime goal : _____   Shoot out goal : _____   Game winning goal : ☐

Penalties : _____   Penality minutes : _____   +/- : _____   Hits : _____

Favorite game memory : _____
_____

Game Notes : _____
_____
_____
_____
_____
_____
_____
_____

FINAL SCORE			VISITOR
			HOME

Date : _____ **Hockey league level :** _____

City : _____

Arena : _____

My Team : _____

Opponent : _____

Position : _____ **Jersey Number :** _____

Goals : _____ **Assists :** _____ **Points :** _____ **Shots taken :** _____

Power play goals : _____ **Short handed goals :** _____

Overtime goal : _____ **Shoot out goal :** _____ **Game winning goal :** ☐

Penalties : _____ **Penality minutes :** _____ **+/- :** _____ **Hits :** _____

Favorite game memory : _____
_____

Game Notes : _____
_____
_____
_____
_____
_____
_____

FINAL SCORE			VISITOR
			HOME

Date : _____ Hockey league level : _____

City : _____

Arena : _____

My Team : _____

Opponent : _____

Position : _____ Jersey Number : _____

Goals : _____ Assists : _____ Points : _____ Shots taken : _____

Power play goals : _____ Short handed goals : _____

Overtime goal : _____ Shoot out goal : _____ Game winning goal : ☐

Penalties : _____ Penality minutes : _____ +/- : _____ Hits : _____

Favorite game memory : _____

_____

Game Notes : _____

_____

_____

_____

_____

_____

_____

_____

FINAL SCORE			VISITOR
			HOME

Date : _____ Hockey league level : _____

City : _____

Arena : _____

My Team : _____

Opponent : _____

Position : _____ Jersey Number : _____

Goals : _____ Assists : _____ Points : _____ Shots taken : _____

Power play goals : _____ Short handed goals : _____

Overtime goal : _____ Shoot out goal : _____ Game winning goal : ☐

Penalties : _____ Penality minutes : _____ +/- : _____ Hits : _____

Favorite game memory : _____
_____

Game Notes : _____
_____
_____
_____
_____
_____
_____
_____

FINAL SCORE			VISITOR
			HOME

Date : _____ Hockey league level : _____

City : _____

Arena : _____

My Team : _____

Opponent : _____

Position : _____ Jersey Number : _____

Goals : _____ Assists : _____ Points : _____ Shots taken : _____

Power play goals : _____ Short handed goals : _____

Overtime goal : _____ Shoot out goal : _____ Game winning goal : ☐

Penalties : _____ Penality minutes : _____ +/- : _____ Hits : _____

Favorite game memory : _____
_____

Game Notes : _____
_____
_____
_____
_____
_____
_____

125

Made in the USA
Columbia, SC
01 May 2023

15970411R00072